HOPSCOTCH

AND OTHER
PLAYGROUND GAMES

HOPSCOTCH
AND OTHER
PLAYGROUND GAMES

Nigel Gross

Illustrated by Chris Pavely

This is a Parragon Book
This edition published in 2003

Parragon
Queen Street House
4 Queen Street
Bath BA1 1HE, UK

Copyright © Parragon 2002

Designed, produced and packaged by
Stonecastle Graphics Limited

Text by Nigel Gross
Illustrated by Chris Pavely
Edited by Gillian Haslam

ISBN 1-40540-406-X

Printed in China

Contents

First Things First

You're going to have great fun with the games and activities in this book, but before we start, here are four very important things to remember.

- Always ask a grown-up before you start chalking
- Never chalk on other people's property unless you have their permission
- Always clean up after you have finished playing .
- Always be safe and don't play near busy traffic

OK then, that's the grown-up bit out of the way... let's talk about the fun things.

This book is all about games you can play outside. There are lots of different sorts — some you'll have to think about, some will need a steady aim and others will need a lot of jumping about. Come to think of it, there's probably something for everybody. You can even play some of them with a pencil and paper if it's raining outside.

Chalky the Owl will be around to show you how to do things... he's pretty cool for a wise old owl!

Anyway that's enough talking, let's get those chalks out and start playing.

Making a Shooter

Quite a few of the games in this book need a shooter. Flat stones or coins are fine but it's much better to make one out of a bottle top. The sort of top you need is called a 'Crown Cap'. These usually come on beer bottles so it's best to ask a grown-up to find you some.

Once you have some bottle tops you need to give them some extra weight, so they don't flip over when you flick or kick them. There are several ways to do this, but the easiest is to press some Plasticine or modelling clay into it. If you want, you can paint your shooter as well, so that you'll know which is yours during a game. If you do decide to paint it, it's best to varnish it as well, so the paint doesn't rub off. Remember to check with a grown-up before you use paint or varnish.

For some of the games you might want to have a shooter that's a bit softer than a bottle top. You can use a small bean bag for this. You can easily make one by filling a small bag with peanut shells or rice. Ask a grown-up to help you make a bag out of cloth. A strong plastic bag with a knot in it is almost as good though — but remember, don't make it too big — a 6cm square is fine.

Chalky's Masterclass

All through this book you'll come across games where you will have to flick or kick the shooter. This takes quite a bit of skill to do well so here are a few tips from Chalky.

The Flick

There are two ways to do this and the one you use is up to you.

The first is called the Thumb Flick. Hold your thumb with your index finger and balance the shooter on your thumbnail. Now flick your thumb. The shooter travels through the air and can be very accurate, though it will bounce a lot.

The other way is the Finger Flick. Here the shooter stays on the ground and you flick it with your index finger. It doesn't bounce as much as the Thumb Flick, but any lumps and bumps in the ground can put it way off target.

The Kick

You don't want to kick the shooter like a football as you will lose it in no time and it can be dangerous. The way to do it is to imagine you're kicking the ground just in front of it, so your foot only just touches the shooter. You'll get a lot more control this way.

Number Noughts and Crosses

This game is a clever version of the old Noughts and Crosses game. (Some people call this Tic-Tac-Toe — don't worry, it's the same game.)

Instead of playing with O's and X's you use the numbers 1 to 10 instead. One player uses the odd numbers (1, 3, 5, 7, 9) and the other the even ones (2, 4, 6, 8, 10).

Number of players: Two

Each player takes it in turns, in exactly the same way as normal Noughts and Crosses, but instead of just getting a line you have to make sure the numbers in the line add up to 15 as well!

You can use a number as many times as you want to, and any rows that don't add up to 15 do not score. Lines can be up, down or diagonal.

It's a good idea for each player to use a different colour of chalk. When a player gets a scoring line, mark it through with the winner's coloured chalk. This will help you to keep the score.

Chalky Says:
Grown-ups will like you playing this game because it will help you learn sums... but we know it's great fun as well!

The first player to get 10 scoring lines is the winner.

Noughts and Tosses

This is another variation on the previous game. It's a lot easier than Number Noughts and Crosses, but you have to be a good shot with your shooter.

Number of players: Two
Things you'll need: Your shooter

First draw out the playing grid as you would for normal Noughts and Crosses, but make it big — you'll see why in a minute.

Now take three BIG steps away from it and draw a line. (You can make it even further if you want but the game will be much harder!)

Both players now stand on this line and take it in turns to toss their shooter, trying to make it land in one of the spaces on the playing grid. If a player manages to do this, then they mark that space with either a Nought or Cross. The first player to get a full line wins.

Lines can be across, down or diagonal.

A shooter must not be touching any lines to score (that's why the grid must be bigger than normal).

Chalky Says:
Remember the shooter might bounce, so don't play where you might lose it. A drain can be a pain... Gosh, what a poet I am!

Boxing Clever

The first thing you need to do is to draw out a large grid of dots, just like in the picture. You can have as many dots as you want, but they all have to be drawn in straight lines. The more dots you have, the longer the game will last.

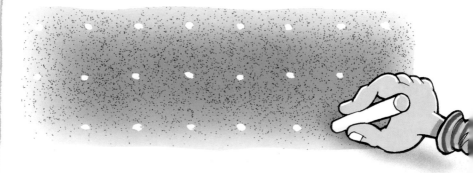

Number of players: Best with two, but up to four is OK

Each player now takes it in turns to connect two dots together with a line. The dots have to be next to each other and diagonal lines are not allowed. The aim of the game is to make boxes. You do this by drawing in the last side of a box.

If a player manages to make a box they get another go. As long as you can keep making boxes, then you carry on with your turn.

Once a player makes a box they mark it with their initial.

When all of the grid has been boxed in, count up how many boxes each player has completed. The one with the highest score is the overall winner.

Chalky Says:
This game gets quite tricky towards the end so be very careful where you put that line.

Snake

This game is also called Serpent or Zig Zag.

The first thing you have to do is to draw out a grid of dots, just like the one you needed to play Boxing Clever (see page 14). The more players you have the more dots you should have. It's also a good idea to make the grid a bit bigger as well so people don't have to squeeze together.

Number of players: As many as you like

The first player draws a line between any two dots (the dots must be next to each other). This line can be up, across or diagonal. The next player then continues this line to the next dot. They can start at either end.

Players now continue to add to either end of the line. Now here's where the tricky bits come in!

A line cannot cross another line and you cannot make any kind of closed shape.

If a player cannot draw a line without doing one of these things they are knocked out. The last player left is the winner.

Chalky Says:
You need to think ahead in this game... it can really get tricky at the end.

Hopscotch

Hopscotch is a game about throwing, hopping and not falling over! It is a very old game... your grandmother probably played it when she was at school and that was a long time ago!

First you must mark out the correct shape on the ground with your chalks. Remember to make the boxes big enough so that your feet will fit inside them.

Number of players: As many as you like
Things you'll need: A small pebble or a bottle top as your shooter

The first player throws their shooter into square one. They must then hop over this and up the course landing with one foot in each square. Where there are two squares next to each other you can put both feet down at the same time (squares 3 & 4 and 6 & 7). When you reach the end box you must turn round and hop back to the beginning.

Once you have done this, you must throw the shooter into square 2 and hop up the course again, then square 3 and so on until you get up to the end.

Chalky Says:
There are quite a few different ways to play this old game, keep a look out later in the book for some more of them.

This all sounds easy doesn't it? Well, if you miss the square with your shooter, or your foot touches a line, you end your turn and the next player has a go... you'll soon see that it's not quite as easy as it first sounds.

The first player to finish the course all eight times is the winner.

Walk the Week

First draw out the playing area as Chalky has here.

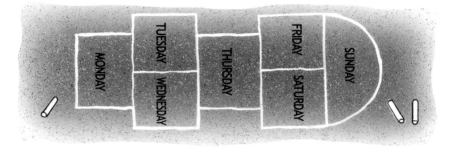

You play this game a little like Hopscotch, but instead of throwing the shooter you have to stand on one leg and kick the shooter with your other foot. TRICKY!

Number of players: As many as you like
Things you'll need: A shooter for each player

The first player pushes their shooter into the Monday box. They then hop over this into the Tuesday box. They then hop through all of the boxes and back to the box with the shooter. They must now kick it into the Tuesday box (remembering to stand on one leg of course!). Once they've done this, they hop through the days of the week and then back to their shooter. Play continues like this until one of the following things happens:

A player moves their shooter through all of the days of the week and is the winner.

If a player falls over, the next player has a go.

If the shooter is pushed into the wrong box or ends up on a line, the next player has a go.

Once a player's turn has finished, their shooter is left where it is until it is their turn again.

Chalky Says:
Remember not to kick your
shooter too hard!

Snail's Race

Draw out the snail shape just like Chalky has done. Remember to make it big enough to stand in.

Number of players: As many as you like

The first player hops from box 1 to box 10 using their right foot, then back to box 1 using their left foot, remembering to hop into every box. If they manage to do this the player puts their initials into box 1. The next player now does the same but cannot hop into a box that already has initials in it — they must hop over it.

Every time a player hops the course they put their initials into a box of their choice.

A player loses their turn if their foot touches a line or they put their foot into a box with another player's initials in it. A player may put both feet into a box with their own initials in it.

The player with their initials in the most boxes at the end of the game is the winner.

Chalky Says:
Choose which box you put your initials in carefully!

Skullies

This is a very old game and needs a lot of skill with the shooter.

First draw out the target just like Chalky has done. Remember to make the boxes big enough to stand in.

Number of players: As many as you like
Things you'll need: A shooter for each player

The first player stands in box 1 and flicks their shooter into box 2. If they manage it, then they move to box 2 and try to do the same into box 3, and so on. If the shooter misses the box or lands on the edges of the box, that player's turn is over. They mark the box they were standing in and the next player has a go.

When everyone has had a turn, the first player plays again, starting from where they left off.

The first player to get from 1 to 12 and then into the skull is the winner.

Chalky Says:
Why this old game has a skull as a target is anyone's guess... I certainly don't know even though I am an extremely wise old owl.

Shoot Out!

This game is all about accuracy. You can choose to make the game easier or more difficult by changing how far away the players stand from the target. First draw out the target just like Chalky has done.

Number of players: Best with at least three
Things you'll need: A shooter for each player

Players take it in turns to flick their shooter at the target. If a shooter misses or lands on a line, they do not score. If you manage to land your shooter on the bull's-eye then you get another go. Once all the players have had a go, the shooters are collected up and play starts again.

Just to make things more interesting, if you manage to hit another player's shooter you score a bonus point.

The first player to score 20 points is the winner.

Chalky Says:
You need to be a good shot with the shooter for this game, and don't forget to keep your score!

Heartbreaker

First chalk out the heart-shaped target like we have here, and then fill it up with as many smaller hearts as will fit. Write 'Love me' in half of them and 'Love me not' in the other half. Decide how far you are going to stand away from the target and draw a line.

Number of players: As many as you like
Things you'll need: A shooter

The players take it in turns to stand on the line and flick their shooter at the target.

To score, a shooter must be more than half in a small heart.

Every time a shooter lands in a small heart the player puts their initials in it.

If a shooter lands in a small heart that already belongs to another player then they miss a turn.

When all the small hearts have been taken, each player's 'Love me's' are added up and then all their 'Love me not's' are taken away.

The player with the most 'Love me's' left is the winner.

Chalky Says:
Don't make the small hearts
too small or the game will *be*
too difficult to play.

Hangman

You can play this game with a pencil and paper as well. Although this game is very old it is still great fun to play.

Number of players: Two

One player thinks of a word and then draws out a short line (this is called a 'dash') for every letter in the word they have thought of. The other player now starts to guess the letters in the word.

If the player guesses a letter right, the other player rubs out the dash and replaces it with the letter. For example, if the secret word was Elephant and the other player guessed A, the word would look like this _ _ _ _ _ A _ _. If they then guessed L, it would look like this _ L _ _ _ A _ _, and so on.

Every time a player guesses wrongly the other player can draw in a line of the 'Hanged Man'. Chalky's already drawn one for you here so you can see what it looks like.

If the second player guesses the word before the hangman is all drawn then they win. If they don't, the first player wins.

Chalky Says:
Don't forget to spell words the correct way!

Feather Flight

This game comes all the way from South America. Apparently it was invented to teach children how to throw spears in battle!

Number of players: As many as you like
Things you'll need: A shuttlecock or feathers and a ball of modelling clay

If you don't have a shuttlecock you can make a feather token by sticking several long feathers into a ball of modelling clay. You can usually find some feathers in a park. Searching around duck ponds would be another good place.

Once you have your feather token draw out the target just like Chalky has done, then decide how far you are going to stand away from it and draw a line.

Players take it in turns to stand on the line and throw their feather token at the target. Add up the score from each player. The first to reach 100 points wins. Remember that if any part of the feather token lands on a line then it does not score.

Chalky Says:
Remember that the game gets a lot harder on a windy day.

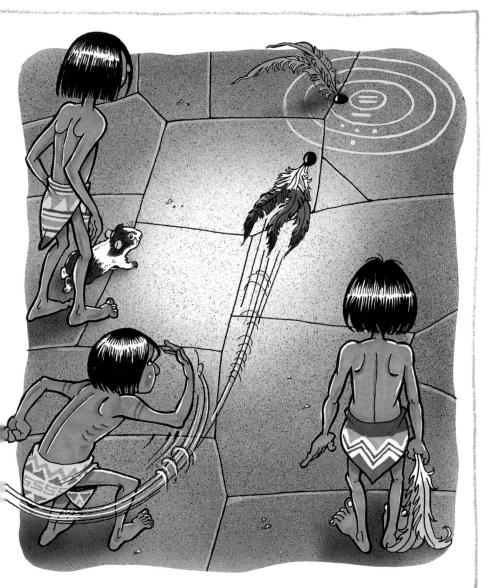

Stake-Out

This game is a little like Skullies (see page 24), but this time the aim is to capture parts of a house rather than catching the skull.

Number of players: As many as you like
Things you'll need: A shooter for each player

Chalk out the target like we have here. You can make it big or small, or even make it look like a castle if you want. Decide how far away you want to stand and draw a line.

Players now take it in turns to stand on the line and flick their shooter at the target.

If a shooter lands cleanly in a part of the house, the player chalks their initials in it.

Shooters must not touch a line — if they do, they don't count.

If a shooter lands in a part of the house already captured by another player, then they miss a turn.

When all of the house has been captured add up the totals for each player. The one with the most is the winner.

Chalky Says:
Try playing this game with the feather token described on page 32 if you fancy a change.

Pavement Golf

You're going to need quite a large area to play this game.

First decide on where you are going to start from and draw a line on the pavement. Now go at least 5m away and draw a circle about 1m across (this is the green). Finally, draw another small circle for the hole somewhere inside the green.

Number of players: As many as you like (you can play this game by yourself as well)
Things you'll need: A shooter for each player

Players take it in turns to kick their shooter gently towards the hole. Once the shooter is on the green, instead of kicking it, they flick it with their finger. This makes accuracy easier — just like putting does in the real game.

Chalky Says:
If you've got the room you
can design a whole golf course
to play on.

To get the shooter in the hole it must be completely inside the small circle.

The player who used the least kicks and flicks to complete the hole wins the game.

You can make the game more difficult by drawing shapes to represent bunkers as well. If any part of a shooter lands in one of these, then that player has an extra point added to their score for that hole.

Sprouts

This game was invented in the USA in the 1960s. You can play it on paper with a pencil if it's raining, but it's much more fun to play it outside on the pavement.

Number of players: This game works best with just two players

First you must draw 5 dots on the ground in any pattern you like. Don't make them too far apart, 30cm would be about right.

The players now take it in turns to draw a line joining two dots together. When they have done this they draw a new dot somewhere on the line they have just drawn.

Each player takes it in turn to do this until there are no more dots to be joined. The last player to join two dots is the winner.

There are just three simple rules:

A dot can only ever have three lines coming from it

A line cannot cross another line

A line cannot go through a dot

Chalky Says:
This game was invented by a mathematician to help prove a really difficult maths problem... now who said sums are dull?

You should have great fun with this — there's a lot more to winning than you might think!

Grand Prix

This game needs a steady aim with the shooter.

Number of players: Best with two
Things you'll need: A shooter for each player

Chalk out the racetrack. To start with
you can copy the one shown here.
It's best to play with this
one until you get used
to the game, then you
can experiment with
your own creations.

Players take it in turns to flick their shooters round the track. If a
shooter touches the edges of the track then it has 'spun off' and that
flick doesn't count. The shooter is placed back where it started and
play passes to the next player.

If a shooter hits another player's shooter, this means there has
been a crash. The player who caused the crash moves his shooter
back to the nearest pit stop.

The winner is the first player to pass the finishing line.

Chalky Says:
This game can be quite tricky to master. Don't be tempted to flick the shooter too hard or you'll spin off the racetrack too often.

Nine Holes

You can also play this game on paper and use coins instead of shooters if you wish.

Number of players: Two
Things you'll need: Three shooters or counters for each player (they must be different shapes or colours, so that you can tell them apart)

Versions of this game have been played for over 6000 years. A board for it was found carved in the foundations of an ancient pyramid in Egypt.

The game itself is a bit like Noughts and Crosses, except that in this game you can actually move the noughts and crosses as well!

Players first take it in turns to place a shooter on one of the dots. When all of the shooters are placed they can start to be moved. Players take it in turns to move one shooter at a time. Shooters can move to any dot next door to it that is empty, but diagonal moves are not allowed.

Chalky Says:
Although this game looks like Noughts and Crosses it's a lot more challenging. It's easy to play – but difficult to play well!

42

The first player to get their shooters in a straight line (just like Noughts and Crosses) is the winner.

Stepping Stones

This game is a sort of race with a difference.

First you need to draw two lines at least 5m apart. Mark one 'Start' and the other 'Finish'. Now mark out a shape like the one Chalky has drawn for you about 2m away.

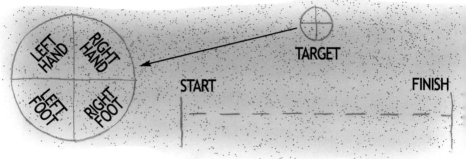

Number of players: As many as you like
Things you'll need: A shooter

The first player stands on the start line and throws their shooter at the target. If they miss, the next player gets a go. If they land in the target they lean forward as far as they can (without touching the ground) and draw a small circle. This circle is called a stepping stone. They then place a hand or foot onto the stepping stone their shooter landed on. They now have another go, slowly moving forward as they do so, until they either miss the target or lose their balance and touch the ground outside their stepping stone.

Once everyone has had a turn the first player has another go and starts from where they left off, but can stand on their stepping stone with both feet.

- Players can only use their own stepping stones
- The first player to get to the finish line is the winner

It's a good idea to have a different coloured chalk for each player so that you can tell which stepping stone belongs to which player.

Chalky Says:
You need to have really good balance to play this game well, and being good with the shooter helps too!

Pavement Beetle

You can also play this game indoors with a dice, pencil and paper if you want to.

First of all, mark out the target as we have here (a circle divided into 6 segments, labelled Head, Body, One Eye, One Leg, One Feeler, Tail). Mark another line a little distance away (the further away this is the more difficult the game will be).

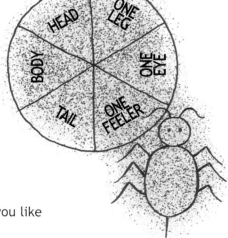

Number of players: As many as you like
Things you'll need: A shooter

Players now take it in turns to stand on the line to flick their shooter at the target. Every time a shooter lands in a segment the player can draw out that part of the beetle. Shooters have to be all in the target. Shooters on lines don't count.

The first player to draw all of the beetle is the winner.

Just to make it more interesting though...

You have to get the body first.

You cannot draw eyes or feelers until you have the head.

Chalky Says:
I quite like the look of that beetle... I think it would make a very tasty supper!

Hoax Ball

This game comes from the Netherlands, where it is very popular during school playtime.

Number of players: At least six
Things you'll need: A ball (any size, but not a hard one!)

First of all, mark out a large circle in chalk on the ground. This should be at least 5m across, so you are going to need quite a large space to play in. Also remember that the ball is going to be thrown so avoid places where the ball might get lost or land somewhere dangerous.

All the players except one now stand around the circle with their toes on the chalk line. They have to have their hands clasped behind their back. The other player takes the ball and stands in the middle of the circle. This player is called the joker.

Chalky Says:
The size of the circle makes a big difference to the difficulty of this game. Please don't throw the ball too hard or aim at a person's head as you might hurt them.

The joker now throws the ball (not too hard!) at a player of their choice. That person must clap their hands and catch the ball. If they fail to do this they are out and leave the circle. The joker continues to throw the ball until there is only one player left.

The last player left is the winner and becomes the joker for the next game.

Giant Pictures

This isn't a game but a fun way to draw really big pictures that will amaze your friends.

Number of players: Can be played by yourself or with as many friends as you want
Things you'll need: A picture to copy, pencil and a ruler

The first thing you need to do is to find an area of pavement that is made of square slabs. If you can see it from an upstairs window, this is even better.

Now you need to find a picture to copy, which should be fairly easy to draw. Now take the pencil and ruler and draw a grid over the picture — Chalky's already done one for you here. Remember to check with a grown-up before you draw on a picture.

Once you have the picture divided up into boxes, go outside and look at the pavement. Imagine that one of the small boxes on your picture equals one of the paving slabs. Draw the contents of the small box onto the paving slab with your chalk. Do this for each box/slab and you'll soon have a giant copy of the picture. This is a lot easier than it sounds, and if you don't tell people how you did it they will be amazed.

If you can get above the picture (such as looking from an upstairs window) the effect is even better. Remember not to lean out too far or do anything dangerous!

Pavement Artist

This isn't really a game but a few ideas to get you going.

Using your chalks to draw on the pavement can be just as much fun as playing games. You can do it by yourself as well, which is great for when your friends aren't around.

Here are a few ideas for you:

If you like playing with model cars, why not draw out a town with lots of roads for them to drive around on?

Get one of your friends to lie on the ground and then draw around them. Then you can draw their face and clothes inside the outline, and colour them in.

Chalky Says:
Really let your imagination run wild... it's the only limit to the fun you can have!

Try drawing the top half of an animal (it can be anything you like) and then carefully cover it up with something, with just the very bottom edge of it showing. Get a friend to draw in the bottom half. They don't know what you've drawn and the results can be very funny!

Look for cracks or holes in the pavement and then do a drawing that uses these. For instance, some cracks look like spiders' legs, others are like the eyes of some horrible monster!

Sidewalk Slalom

This game is like the slalom obstacle course for skiers.

Number of players: As many as you like
Things you'll need: A shooter or small ball, and a watch

First mark out the course as shown here by Chalky. You vary the number of gates and the length of the course to suit yourselves.

Players take it in turns to kick the shooter as quickly as they can through the course. They must go between each pair of chalk marks — these are called gates. One of the players must time this on the watch. Once all the players have had two goes, add their scores together. The player with the lowest overall time is the winner.

For every gate a player misses they get five seconds added to their time. The player with the watch is going to have to keep a good lookout for this!

Chalky Says:
Good shooter control is as
important as speed. Try playing
this game on the beach in
summer. Use small twigs to
make the gates and use a ball
instead. Great fun!

King's Corner

Chalk out the playing area just as Chalky has done. The squares should be about 3m on each side. They can be bigger, but if they are smaller it will make the game more difficult.

KING

Number of players: Four
Things you'll need: A ball — any size will do but it must bounce

One player now stands in each box. The player standing in the box with 'King' written in it takes the ball. This player lets the ball bounce once and then hits it towards any other player. You can use your hands and feet to hit the ball, even your head if you want. The player hitting the ball is called the server. The player receiving the ball must let it bounce once in their square and then hit it on to another player.

Chalky Says:
This game needs a lot of skill to play well. Try using only your feet to hit the ball for an even tougher challenge.

Play continues like this until one of the following things happens:
- A player touches the ball before it has bounced once in their square
- A player does not hit the ball on to another player before it has bounced twice

If either of these things happen the receiving player loses a life.

- A player hits the ball and it does not land in another square

If this happens then the serving player loses a life.

All players start with 10 lives. When they have lost them all they are out, and play continues with three players, then two until the last player left is declared the winner.

Monster's Pie

Chalk out the pie shape like Chalky has done and place the pencil in the middle of it.

Number of players: Four to six
Things you'll need: A pencil

The first player spins the pencil. If it lands in a segment of pie that has a number in it they score that number of points and have another go. Play continues until the pencil ends up pointing at the segment with the monster drawn in it. This player now becomes the judge.

The next player now has a go, and scores points until the pencil points to the monster again. This time all of the players except the judge must shout 'Monster, Monster don't eat me. Monster, Monster don't eat me. Monster, Monster I'm sorry I ate your pie.' They then clap their hands three times. The judge decides who finished last. This player loses 5 points from their score and now becomes the judge.

Play now passes to the next player.

The first player to get 25 points is the winner.

Chalky Says:
It's probably a good idea not to upset the judge when you're playing this game. It might affect their judgement...
Ho ho ho!

Sharks and Castaways

This is a great game to play with a lot of people, especially on a cold day... you'll soon warm up as there's a lot of running about to do.

Number of players: At least eight, but even more is better

You need a large area to play this game properly. Once you've found a good place, chalk out a circle large enough for all of the players except one to stand in. This circle is called the island. Now draw out three other smaller circles a good distance from the island. These are the rescue ships. If you're feeling particularly artistic you could draw them to look like ships as well.

All of the players except one now stand on the island. These are the castaways. The remaining player stays off the island and is called the shark.

Chalky Says:
This game is great fun and
good exercise!

The castaways must escape from the island and get safely to one of the rescue ships. The shark tries to stop them doing this. If the shark manages to touch any castaway once they have left the island then that castaway becomes a shark as well.

When there are no more castaways on the island, all the players who reached the rescue ships safely go back to the island and play continues. The last castaway left is the winner.

Pom Pom

This game is an interesting version of Hide and Seek.

Number of players: As many as you like, but you need at least four for a good game

Chalk a circle large enough for all of the players to stand in. One player now stands in the circle and closes their eyes and counts to 20. This player is called the seeker. The other players now run off and hide (these are called the hiders).

Once the seeker has completed their count they must go off and look for the other players. The hiders must try to get back to the circle and shout 'Pom Pom' when they get there.

If the seeker finds a hider they must race back to the circle and shout Pom Pom and the player's name. If they manage to do this before the hider gets back to the circle and shouts Pom Pom, they have captured the hider.

Once every player is back in the circle, the number of captures is recorded and play starts again with a different player as the seeker. Once every player has had a turn as the seeker the scores are added up. The seeker with the highest number of captures is the winner.

Chalky Says:
Stealth and speed... a great game for an owl I think.

Achi

Here is a slightly more difficult version of Nine Holes (see pages 42-43). It was invented in Ghana, in Africa.

Number of players: Two
Things you'll need: Four shooters for each player (they must be different shapes or colours, so that you can tell them apart)

You start off with 4 shooters each but still only have to get 3 in a row to win. Otherwise the rules are exactly the same as they are for Nine Holes. Chalky has drawn out a small Achi board for you here if you fancy giving it a try.

Chalky Says:
Why not try to make up some of your own games to play with chalk?